# ROY OF THE ROVERS

# ANNUAL

# 1989

Fleetway Publications 1988

£3.50

AT HALF-TIME, TRAINER MERVYN WALLACE WAS WAITING WITH INTERESTING NEWS...

WE'VE GOT A **SPY**, ROY! FOURTH ROW, TO THE LEFT OF THE TUNNEL... RECOGNISE HIM?

HEY, THAT'S **WALLY MORRISON**, MANAGER OF PENDRYTH UNITED! WE PLAY THEM NEXT WEEK IN THE F.A. CUP!

SOUR OLD DEVIL! RUMOUR HAS IT HE WAS MIXED UP IN A COUPLE OF SHADY **TRANSFER DEALS** A FEW YEARS BACK!

LATEST RUMOUR IS HE'LL GET THE **SACK** NEXT WEEK UNLESS HIS TEAM BEATS US IN THE CUP MATCH!

PENDRYTH HAVE LOST SEVEN GAMES IN A ROW! THE BOARD WANTS A NEW WINNING FORMULA — **OR MORRISON GETS THE CHOP!**

SO NOW HE'S COME LOOKING FOR A WEAK LINK IN THE MELCHESTER LINE-UP! THE WAY WE'RE PLAYING TODAY I FEEL **SORRY** FOR THAT GUY, MERV!

IN THE DRESSING-ROOM...

HEY, WHAT'S HAPPENED TO OUR ORANGE SLICES AND BARLEY SQUASH? WHAT'S **THIS** RUBBISH?

**VEEVAVIT MINERAL WATER FOR EXTRA ENERGY!** THE CLUB DOCTOR RECOMMENDED IT!

I'M PUTTING THE ENTIRE FIRST TEAM SQUAD ON A COURSE OF IT FOR THE NEXT MONTH, SO... **DRINK UP!**

THIS STUFF TASTES LIKE **DISH-WATER!**

THAT'S THE **SULPHUR, SALTS AND IRON** IN VEEVAVIT DOING YOU **GOOD**, McKAY! INSTANT VITALITY — **RIGHT**, ROY?

WELL... ER... **YES**, IF YOU SAY SO, MERVYN! IT DOES TASTE A BIT **STRANGE**, THOUGH!

QUARTER TO ONE! SATURDAY AFTERNOON! YOU SHOULD BE AT UNITED'S **GROUND** BY NOW!

Y-YOU MEAN... SLEPT IN... BUT HOW? WHAT... **WHAT HAPPENED,** DEBBIE?

I DON'T KNOW, MILD FOOD POISONING, MAYBE! SOMETHING IN THE MEAL LAST NIGHT! I DIDN'T EAT WITH YOU, AND I'M OKAY...

BUT YOU AND THE **REST** OF THE TEAM HAVE BEEN CRASHED OUT FOR FOURTEEN HOURS! WE'VE BEEN GOING **FRANTIC** TRYING TO WAKE YOU UP!

*DAZED MELCHESTER PLAYERS MOVED ABOUT LIKE ZOMBIES...*

WE HAVE LESS THAN **TWO HOURS** TO PULL OURSELVES TOGETHER! **NO WAY** WE CAN GET THE F.A. TO POSTPONE A CUP GAME AT **THIS** LATE STAGE!

*SOMEHOW THEY MADE IT TO UNITED'S GROUND... **AND A** SESSION OF ICE-COLD SHOWERS!*

NUUU-UUH! YEEE-AAH!

C-CAN'T STAND IT! CAN'T **TAKE** ANY MORE!

SHUT UP—**ALL** OF YOU! NOBODY COMES OUT OF THERE UNTIL HE'S **BUTTON BRIGHT AND WIDE AWAKE!**

*BUT IT WAS EASIER SAID THAN DONE! ONLY MINUTES BEFORE KICK-OFF...*

THERE GOES THE BELL, BOSS... AND ANDY STYLES IS **ASLEEP** AGAIN!

ZZZ-ZZZZZZ!

THEN BOOT HIM OFF THAT BENCH, SLAP HIS FACE, DO **ANYTHING,** BUT GET HIM ON HIS FEET!

*IN THE TUNNEL...*

HELLO, RACE, GLAD TO SEE YOUR **ANKLE'S** OKAY AGAIN! COULD BE A CLOSE GAME THIS AFTERNOON! HA, HA, HA!

*WALLY MORRISON, GRINNING ALL OVER HIS FACE! SOMEBODY MUST HAVE TOLD HIM WHAT HAPPENED AT THE HOTEL!*

10

Liverpool's John Barnes heads clear during a Coventry City on-slaught.

# ROY RACE ENQUIRY

# THE SUPER

**Is there too much football? Should the First Division be stream-lined?**

A Super League...it's been a topic of discussion for many years in soccer.

Some people feel it would be in football's best interests to streamline the First Division to 10 or 12 clubs, rather like the Premier Division in Scotland.

Scottish soccer is booming, with increasing gates and their clubs paying the sort of transfer fees that not so long ago they RECEIVED from English clubs. Now the trend has reversed.

Graeme Souness, the Glasgow Rangers manager, has spent millions on top English players such as Chris Woods, Terry Butcher, Graham Roberts and Ray Wilkins.

But many critics feel there is already a Super League within the English First Division. And when you look at the clubs who have won the Championship in recent years, it's a difficult point to argue with.

Liverpool and Everton have dominated the title honours during the Eighties. And it is becomingly increasingly difficult for smaller clubs to win the Championship.

The reason is...money. While the big clubs get richer the small clubs get...well, if not poorer, they are becoming the poor relations.

Kenny Dalglish, the Liverpool manager, has spent more than £5 million on strengthening his squad. As someone joked, with that money they should win the Boat Race, too!

Much of that outlay came from the £3.2 million Juventus paid for Ian Rush. But Liverpool's massive support also enabled Dalglish to buy John Aldridge, John Barnes, Peter

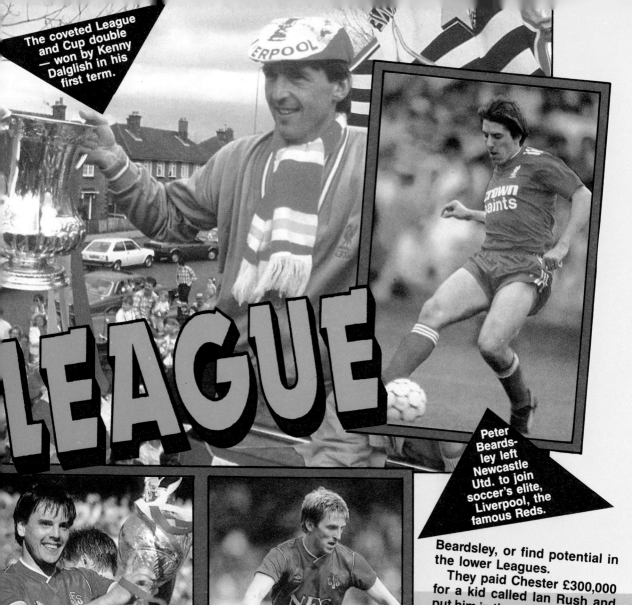

The coveted League and Cup double — won by Kenny Dalglish in his first term.

Peter Beardsley left Newcastle Utd. to join soccer's elite, Liverpool, the famous Reds.

Two shining Everton stars. Graeme Sharp and (right) Gary Stevens.

# LEAGUE

Beardsley, or find potential in the lower Leagues.

They paid Chester £300,000 for a kid called Ian Rush and put him in the reserves to 'learn his trade' and play the Liverpool way. Look what happened when Rush learnt quickly!

While most clubs have to rely on finding their own talent, for financial reasons, super-rich Liverpool can buy who they want. As one chairman said: "We're like little corner shops waiting to be taken over by a supermarket."

Still, no-one can doubt Liverpool's way has been successful.

Everton, too, have traditionally bought big, although more than Liverpool they have also found their own stars.

However, Merseyside fans have been bred on big names and like Liverpool, Everton are expected to be in the market whenever a top class player becomes available.

They paid close on £1 million

Beardsley, Nigel Spackman and Ray Houghton.

Last season, Liverpool had 'reserves' such as Danish international Jan Molby who would walk into just about any other first Division side. Dalglish even substituted £1.8 million

Beardsley, Britain's costliest player!

Liverpool tend to buy their players rather than produce them themselves through the youth team. Their policy has been either to buy a ready-made star, such as Barnes or

# THE SUPER LEAGUE

for Norwich centre-half Dave Watson and last season, when they lost the influential Kevin Sheedy through injury, manager Colin Harvey went out and bought Leicester's Ian Wilson for £300,000 as a replacement while the Republic of Ireland midfielder was sidelined.

Like Dalglish, Harvey would rather have good players at his disposal than playing against his side!

Of all the leading clubs, Arsenal have had the best results with their youth policy. Michael Thomas, Tony Adams, David Rocastle, Paul Davis... just a few of the home-bred players who have saved the Gunners a fortune in the transfer market.

Manager George Graham was upset when he lost right-back Viv Anderson to Manchester United when the England star was at the end of his contract.

Instead of panicking and buying a replacement, Graham gave young Thomas his chance and was handsomely rewarded as the England Under-21 defender quickly established himself in the side.

Adams has a touch of the Bobby Moores about him...like the former England captain and defender, Adams is cool under pressure and never seems flustered. He reads the game so well that he is usually one move ahead of opponents.

But Graham hasn't been afraid to enter the transfer market...even if he had been a little conservative compared with Liverpool and Everton.

He paid Leicester £700,000 for striker Alan Smith, whose subtle skills made him a favourite with the Highbury crowd at once .

When Alex Ferguson left Aberdeen in 1986 to take over from Ron Atkinson at Manchester United, he took a long look at his team before deciding what needed to be done.

Ferguson then spent more than £1 million on Arsenal full-back Viv Anderson and Celtic striker Brian McClair.

Hardly a gamble — both players had proved themselves with their previous teams, in Anderson's case he was a European Cup winner with Nottingham Forest.

However, past glories do not guarantee future success, although it didn't take Anderson or McClair long to prove to the critical Old Trafford crowd, bred on world-class players such as George Best, Denis Law and Bobby Charlton, that

Arsenal's Paul Davis causes problems for the Derby County defence.

Tony Adams, the Gunners' young England defender.

14

## ROY says—

"I believe the formation of a Super League would inject superior skills into the game, and bring the crowds flocking back."

Viv Anderson — nicknamed Spider because of his long legs — effective both in defence and attack.

they were worthy of the famous red shirt.

Anderson's nickname is Spider, because of his long legs which he uses to great effect in winning the ball...and joining in the attack overlapping down the right.

United hadn't had a prolific goalscorer for 20 years — since Best or Law, really — but McClair started to reward Ferguson with a flurry of goals at the start of 1987/88.

Tottenham Hotspur have never been afraid to spend big, although they have still managed to retain a flourishing youth scheme. Glenn Hoddle, probably the most naturally gifted English player of the Eighties, came through the ranks at White Hart Lane before joining French club Monaco for £1 million in 1987.

Spurs have also been big sellers — they received £1.5 million from Glasgow Rangers for Richard Gough, who doubled in value in a year after joining the Londoners from Dundee United for £750,000 in 1986!

Liverpool, Everton, Manchester United, Arsenal and

Spurs' high-scoring Clive Allen tries to pass Watford defenders.

High kicks at White Hart Lane between Paul Allen and Man. Utd's Mike Duxbury.

The evergreen Ray Clemence — as safe as ever in the Spurs' goal.

# THE SUPER LEAGUE

long Rangers and Celtic dominated the Scottish scene. But during the Eighties Aberdeen and Dundee United swung the balance of power away from Glasgow to the North-East.

Now, Hearts have a team who can beat the best, which makes for some cracking Premier Division matches.

Graeme Souness took his spending to £4 million when he paid Paris St. Germaine £250,000 for Ray Wilkins, but Celtic, not to be outdone, hit back with transfers such as Frank McAvennie (£750,000 from West Ham) and Joe Miller (£650,000 from Aberdeen).

There has been talk about a British Cup, although in an already crowded fixture list it's difficult to see how another competition could be squeezed in.

The ultimate would probably be an England v Scotland clash in the European Cup Final. Maybe one day we'll see Liverpool v Rangers or Everton v Celtic for the right to be Champions of Europe.

In the meantime, let the discussions continue!

Spurs...they are the Big Five of English football who have been contesting their own Super League — the Super League of money.

But wouldn't it be exciting if those five clubs could join forces with five of the best from Scotland? Celtic v Arsenal... Rangers v Liverpool...Aberdeen v Manchester United... maybe then we would find out who is Britain's greatest?

Scottish football has never been more competitive. For so

# SPOTLIGHT ON...

## KEVIN RATCLIFFE  Everton

Everton's inspirational captain led them to two Championships in three seasons as well as the European Cup-winners' Cup and was unlucky not to be named Footballer of the Year. Seen here with the 1986/87 Championship trophy, Kevin is also the captain of Wales, but the Welsh face an uphill task to qualify for the 1990 World Cup finals with West Germany and Holland in their group. Kevin's pace makes him a match for any striker while he is a calming influence to all when things get tough on the field.

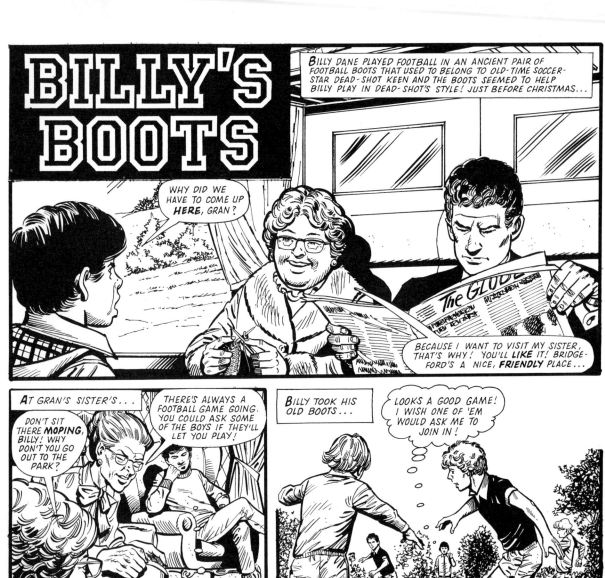

# BILLY'S BOOTS

BILLY DANE PLAYED FOOTBALL IN AN ANCIENT PAIR OF FOOTBALL BOOTS THAT USED TO BELONG TO OLD-TIME SOCCER-STAR DEAD-SHOT KEEN AND THE BOOTS SEEMED TO HELP BILLY PLAY IN DEAD-SHOT'S STYLE! JUST BEFORE CHRISTMAS...

WHY DID WE HAVE TO COME UP **HERE**, GRAN?

BECAUSE I WANT TO VISIT MY SISTER, THAT'S WHY! YOU'LL **LIKE** IT! BRIDGEFORD'S A NICE, **FRIENDLY** PLACE...

AT GRAN'S SISTER'S...

DON'T SIT THERE **MOPING**, BILLY! WHY DON'T YOU GO OUT TO THE PARK?

THERE'S ALWAYS A FOOTBALL GAME GOING. YOU COULD ASK SOME OF THE BOYS IF THEY'LL LET YOU PLAY!

MIGHT AS WELL! BETTER THAN SITTING AROUND HERE!

BILLY TOOK HIS OLD BOOTS...

LOOKS A GOOD GAME! I WISH ONE OF 'EM WOULD ASK ME TO JOIN IN!

AND THEN...

HERE COMES SOMEONE!

WHY DON'T YOU **HOPPIT**? MY PLAYERS ARE COMPLAINING YOU'RE PUTTING 'EM OFF, STANDING THERE LIKE SOMETHING THE CAT BROUGHT IN!

20

23

Many critics call Spurs boss Terry Venables the best coach in English football and there is no doubt his return to Division One in 1987 was a boost for our game. In Spain, "El Tel" won the Championship and took Barcelona to the European Cup Final. The former Spurs midfield player is confident he can restore the glory days to Tottenham as manager...here we take a closer look at the man who may one day become manager of England.

BOSS

QPR O, Spurs I...FA Cup Final replay 1982. As manager of Rangers, Venables led them to Wembley and here Galvin of Spurs (left) tussles with QPR's Gregory.

# ON THE MOVE

El Tel and Spurs' Argentine Ossie Ardiles... speaking in English, of course!

Venables gets a feel of English football's first artificial pitch at Rangers' Loftus Road home in 1981.

Venables with Spurs' goal ace Clive Allen.

Venables in Barcelona with his assistant Allan Harris (left) and Steve Archibald who cost £900,000 from Spurs.

29

30

31

32

GROO-AGH!

GAAGH!

A CANNONBALL SHOT! THERE'S NUMBER THREE!

AFTER THAT, CULTHORPE WENT TO PIECES...AND WITH ANOTHER GOAL FROM BIG BERTHA, THE GIRLS EMERGED CLEAR WINNERS BY FOUR GOALS TO TWO!

LOOK, FREDDIE! JUST TO ADD INSULT TO INJURY, THERE'S THAT MYSTERIOUS BLOKE AGAIN... THE 'FIXER'!

A FANTASTIC GAME, GENTLEMEN! NOW STUMP UP, PLEASE ...FIVE POUNDS A HEAD FOR THE WINNERS' TRIP TO LONDON!

A FIVER! THIS IS MY WHOLE ALLOWANCE FOR A MONTH!

BEING BEATEN BY A TEAM OF GIRLS IS BAD ENOUGH, BUT TO BE ROBBED AS WELL, IS—

POETIC JUSTICE, I'D SAY!

F-FREDDIE, IT AIN'T POSSIBLE...IS IT? TH-THAT 'FIXER' IS NO BLOKE! HE—I MEAN SHE—IS YOUR SISTER JANE!

GOOD DISGUISE, EH? I EVEN SLIPPED A GRANITE CHIP IN MY MOUTH SO THAT I'D SPEAK IN A GRAVEL-VOICE!

THIS IS THE NEW SCHOOL I WON THE SCHOLARSHIP TO— AND WHEN I FOUND OUT THAT THEY RAN A HIGHLY-EFFICIENT GIRLS' FOOTBALL TEAM, I DECIDED TO TAKE YOU BIG-HEADED LOT DOWN A PEG OR TWO!

MISS PRISM, THE SPORTS' MISTRESS HELPED ME TO SET UP THE WHOLE SCHEME! SHE THOUGHT THE SHOCK OF HAVING TO PLAY A GIRLS' TEAM MIGHT PROVE YOUR UNDOING!

BUT I WOULDN'T WORRY TOO MUCH ABOUT LOSING YOUR MONEY, FREDDIE! YOU SEE, THE SPORTS' FUND IS GOING TO MATCH THE £55 YOUR TEAM HAS GIVEN US!

YES, SO BOTH THE WINNERS AND THE LOSERS CAN GO TO LONDON FOR A FABULOUS WEEK-END TREAT! WHAT DO YOU SAY TO THAT, BIG-HEAD?

PLEASE STOP CALLING ME THAT, JANE! I'LL NEVER BOAST ABOUT THE CULTHORPE TEAM AGAIN! AND THAT'S A PROMISE!

THE END.

Douglas...his name may be British but the defender is very Brazilian in his style.

Junior...a great full-back or schemer.

The way the South Americans play soccer is an education in skill and grace. They feint, they sway, they almost dance with the ball in time to the music from their football-loving supporters...

SAMB

Muller...the Brazilian named after West German ace Gerd Muller.

England Captain Bryan Robson under pressure from Brazil's Ricardo.

Scotland v Brazil and it's Murdo MacLeod chasing that man Muller.

A STARS

After making a huge impression on Brazil's 1987 tour of Britain, Mirandinha signed for Newcastle and quickly showed that Brazilian skill can still flourish in a colder climate and a very competitive League. Known in Geordieland as Mira, the striker is now a hero in Newcastle and is respected by all First Division opponents.

Captain of Argentina — Diego Maradona in action at Wembley in 1987.

Spurs' Ossie Ardiles, a World Cup winner for Argentina in 1978. He has given great service to the North London club.

Italy captain Allesandro Altobelli (left) and Maradona flank former Brazil ace Pele.

# JACK of UNITED

JACK CHELSEY BEGAN HIS PROFESSIONAL FOOTBALL CAREER WITH CASTLEBURN UNITED ON THE VERY DAY THAT HIS BROTHER SIGNED FOR THEIR NEAR NEIGHBOURS, CASTLEBURN CITY. CITY MANAGER IAN CLARK SHREWDLY REALISED THAT THE BROTHERS WOULD BE EVEN GREATER PLAYERS IF THEY WERE IN THE SAME TEAM, AND EVENTUALLY PERSUADED UNITED TO TRANSFER JACK TO CITY...

A MARVELLOUS GOAL FROM JIMMY!

BUT IT WAS JACK WHO SET IT UP!

THEY MAKE A GREAT PAIR!

AFTER THE MATCH CLIVE AND PAT, JACK AND JIMMY'S YOUNGER BROTHER AND SISTER, LEFT THE STADIUM WITH SOME FRIENDS...

JIMMY WON THE MATCH WITH THAT GOAL—BUT YOU MUST ADMIT HE'D NEVER HAVE SCORED IT BUT FOR THE WAY JACK SET IT UP.

THEN YOU'VE GOT TO ADMIT THAT JACK IS LUCKY TO HAVE JIMMY THERE TO PUT THE FINISHING TOUCHES!

TRUE. IT'S THE *PARTNERSHIP* THAT MAKES THEM UNIQUE. YET IT MIGHT NEVER HAVE COME ABOUT. THERE WAS A TIME WHEN JACK ALMOST CHUCKED UP FOOTBALL. HE MIGHT WELL HAVE DONE, BUT FOR JIMMY.

I NEVER KNEW THAT. TELL US ABOUT IT, CLIVE.

WAIT UNTIL WE GET TO THE YOUTH CLUB. IT'S EASIER TO TALK THERE.

AND SO CLIVE BEGAN HIS STORY...

OF COURSE, EVERYBODY KNOWS THAT ALTHOUGH JIMMY HAS ALWAYS PLAYED FOR CITY, JACK BEGAN HIS CAREER WITH UNITED, AND HE HAD A MUCH TOUGHER TIME OF IT THAN JIMMY, TO START WITH. UNITED HAD A SUPER SENIOR SQUAD, AND JACK HAD TO STRUGGLE HARD TO KEEP A PLACE IN THE TEAM.

UNITED MANAGER ERIC MILLS BELIEVED IN TAKING HIS TIME BEFORE MAKING UP HIS MIND ABOUT ANY PLAYER. UNITED WERE LOCKED IN A GOAL-LESS DRAW WITH IRONCASTLE.

YOU'VE GOT A GOOD 'UN IN JACK CHELSEY, ERIC. WHY DON'T YOU SET HIS MIND AT REST BY MAKING HIM OFFICIALLY A MEMBER OF THE SENIOR SQUAD?

IT'S A BIT SOON FOR THAT, JOE. IN HIS OWN INTERESTS, HE NEEDS TIME TO DEVELOP.

IAN CLARK, OVER AT CITY, BELIEVES IN DRASTIC METHODS. HE RECKONS IT BRINGS OUT THE BEST IN A PLAYER TO PLUNGE HIM RIGHT IN FROM THE START. I THINK YOU CAN RUIN A LAD THAT WAY.

40

OF COURSE HE'S RIGHT. I ALWAYS USED TO RECKON I WAS IN PRETTY GOOD SHAPE, BUT MY STAMINA ISN'T UP TO UNITED'S STANDARDS. I'VE GOT TO IMPROVE IT...

MONDAY MORNING CAME, AND WHEN CLIVE LOOKED INTO JACK'S ROOM...

I MIGHT HAVE KNOWN THERE'D BE NO NEED TO ROUSE YOU, JACK. MUM SAYS BREAKFAST IN FIVE MINUTES.

CLIVE WENT ON TO JIMMY'S ROOM...

COME ON, JIMMY, YOU SHOULD FOLLOW JACK'S EXAMPLE. HE'S IN THERE DOING PRESS-UPS.

WHAT FOR ? DOESN'T HE GET ENOUGH EXERCISE DURING TRAINING TIME ? I DO. BED ROOMS ARE FOR SLEEPING IN !

AT BREAKFAST...

NO COOKED BREAKFAST, THANKS, MUM ! I HAVE TO WATCH MY WEIGHT. JUST TOAST AND MARMALADE.

GOOD. I'LL HAVE YOUR SHARE, JACK. THERE ARE NO DIET RULES AT CITY.

AT UNITED, THE FIRST HOUR ON MONDAY MORNING WAS DEVOTED TO A PHYSICAL CHECK-UP...

IS THAT JACK'S REPORT ? I'D BETTER HAVE A WORD WITH HIM.

JACK, THIS CONFIRMS THE IMPRESSION I FORMED AGAINST IRONCASTLE. WE'VE BEEN PUSHING YOU AHEAD TOO FAST. I'M TAKING YOU OFF TRAINING FOR A FEW DAYS. GO HOME AND RELAX...

WHAT ? YOU MEAN I'M BEING DROPPED-?

THE BOSS HASN'T SAID THAT.

NO, I HAVEN'T. AND IF I EVER SHOULD, IT WOULD BE BECAUSE I WAS SURE IT WAS FOR YOUR OWN GOOD IN THE LONG RUN.

JACK DIDN'T GO HOME, NOR DID HE TELL THE FAMILY WHAT HAD HAPPENED. NEXT MORNING HE LEFT THE HOUSE AS IF FOR TRAINING AS USUAL...

HOP IN, JACK. I'LL GIVE YOU A LIFT AS FAR AS THE STADIUM.

ER...NO, THANKS, JIM, I'LL WALK. YOU SHOULD DO IT MORE INSTEAD OF RIDING EVERYWHERE IN THAT CAR...

AS SOON AS JIMMY WAS OUT OF SIGHT, JACK CAUGHT A BUS GOING IN THE OPPOSITE DIRECTION...

METROPOL

THAT FELLER WILL MAKE HIMSELF DIZZY! HE'S BEEN RUNNING ROUND AND ROUND THE PARK ALL THE MORNING!

FRIDAY CAME, AND ERIC MILLS MADE HIS CHOICE OF THE TEAM THAT WOULD BE PLAYING AT MANDOVER THE FOLLOWING DAY...

I SEE YOU'RE KEEPING JACK CHELSEY IN AT NO. 6.

I'M BANKING THAT THESE FEW DAYS LAY-OFF FROM STRENUOUS TRAINING WILL HAVE HELPED HIS STAYING POWER.

IT WORRIES ME A LITTLE THAT HE'S LOSING WEIGHT... SUGGESTS THAT I'VE BEEN WORKING HIM TOO HARD. IF I DIDN'T KNOW HIS MOTHER WELL, I'D THINK SHE WASN'T FEEDING HIM WELL ENOUGH!

IT CAN'T BE THAT. I'VE BEEN ROUND THERE FOR MEALS. MRS CHELSEY IS A TERRIFIC COOK.

EARLY IN THE MATCH AT MANDOVER JACK WAS IN STORMING FORM!

WELL DONE, JACK!

JACK ANGLED THE BALL TO GRAHAM MORTLAKE WHO, WHEN TACKLED, PUSHED IT BACK TO HIM.

HAVE A GO YOURSELF, JACK!

GOSH! THERE WAS SOME POWER BEHIND THAT ONE!

THE GOALIE MUST HAVE FELT IT, TOO. I BET IT HURT. LOOK AT HIS FACE.

JACK'S SHAPING WELL!

SO FAR— SO GOOD!

MINUTES LATER, ANOTHER POWERFUL ASSAULT BY JACK ENABLED NORMAN HAMPTON TO PUT THE BALL IN THE BACK OF THE NET!

A GREAT GOAL!

UNITED ARE ONE UP!

UNITED DOMINATED THE GAME UNTIL EARLY IN THE SECOND HALF, THEN MANDOVER BEGAN TO COME BACK...

DON'T LET HIM GET AWAY FROM YOU, JACK!

MANDOVER ALMOST EQUALISED THEN!

THEIR STRIKER MOVED TOO FAST FOR JACK.

A LITTLE LATER JACK MISSED A GOOD CHANCE TO GET THE UNITED ATTACK MOVING.

JACK'S RUN OUT OF STEAM. WE'D BETTER HAVE HIM OFF.

JACK!

THE MANAGER IS SENDING A SUBSTITUTE ON IN MY PLACE. IN SPITE OF ALL MY EFFORTS, I'VE DONE EVEN WORSE THAN IN OUR LAST GAME.

JACK WATCHED GLUMLY AS UNITED RECOVERED THEIR GRIP ON THE GAME, AND WENT FURTHER AHEAD.

2-0 TO UNITED! THAT MUST MAKE IT SAFE!

THEY'RE DOING BETTER WITHOUT ME. I'M BEGINNING TO THINK FOOTBALL JUST ISN'T THE CAREER FOR ME...

A FEW MORNINGS LATER, THE POSTMAN HANDED JIMMY A PUZZLING PACKAGE...

WHY SHOULD ANYONE THINK I WANT TO TRAIN FOR A CAREER IN ELECTRONICS? I'M NOT GIVING UP FOOTBALL!

THIS MUST BE MEANT FOR JACK. BUT WHAT'S HE UP TO? WHY HAS HE BEEN ACTING STRANGELY AND REFUSING A LIFT TO THE STADIUM? IT'S TIME I FOUND OUT.

J. CHELSEY

JIMMY KEPT WATCH...

THAT BUS DOESN'T EVEN PASS THE UNITED GROUND. IT'S HEADING IN THE OPPOSITE DIRECTION. WHERE'S JACK GOING?

JIMMY ARRIVED AT THE PARK TO FIND JACK TAKING ON A WHOLE GANG OF BOYS IN A WILD MATCH...

JACK, YOU DAFT TWIT! HOW LONG HAS THIS BEEN GOING ON?

JACK, CAUGHT RED-HANDED, TOLD JIMMY OF HIS WORRY OVER HIS LOSS OF FORM...

I'VE TRAINED HARD, I'VE WATCHED MY DIET, I'VE TRIED TO KEEP MY WEIGHT DOWN. BUT MY GAME STILL DOESN'T GO RIGHT.

YOU STEAMING IDIOT! IF ERIC MILLS HAD WANTED YOU TO DO THOSE THINGS HE'D HAVE SAID SO! YOU'D BETTER COME CLEAN TO HIM ABOUT WHAT YOU'VE BEEN UP TO.

URGED ON BY JIMMY, JACK CONFESSED TO HIS MANAGER, WHO WAS STUNNED...

YOU WERE OVER-TRAINED... TOO TENSE! YOU WERE PUSHING YOURSELF TOO HARD. I WANTED YOU TO RELAX. GO BACK HOME AND DO AS YOU'RE TOLD—AND WE'LL SEE WHAT HAPPENS ON SATURDAY.

THAT SATURDAY UNITED WERE AT HOME TO THAMESBANK, A POWERFUL SIDE WHICH ALWAYS GAVE THEM A HARD MATCH...

THAMESBANK ARE SETTING AN EVEN FASTER PACE THAN USUAL!

THIS'LL REALLY PUT JACK TO THE TEST!

HE'S DOING ALL RIGHT SO FAR, ANYWAY.

MAYBE... BUT IT'S IN THE SECOND HALF THAT THE CRUNCH WILL COME.

AS PLAY MOVED AT HIGH SPEED FROM END TO END BOTH GOALS HAD NARROW ESCAPES.

UNITED CAME CLOSE THEN!

NO CLOSER THAN THAMESBANK HAVE A FEW TIMES!

BUT JACK HASN'T! JUST LOOK AT HIM MOVE...!

THE GAME WENT WELL INTO THE SECOND HALF, AND THERE WAS STILL NO SCORE...

THE PACE OF THE GAME IS SLOWING.

WHAT ELSE CAN YOU EXPECT? THE PLAYERS HAVE RUN THEMSELVES TO A STANDSTILL!

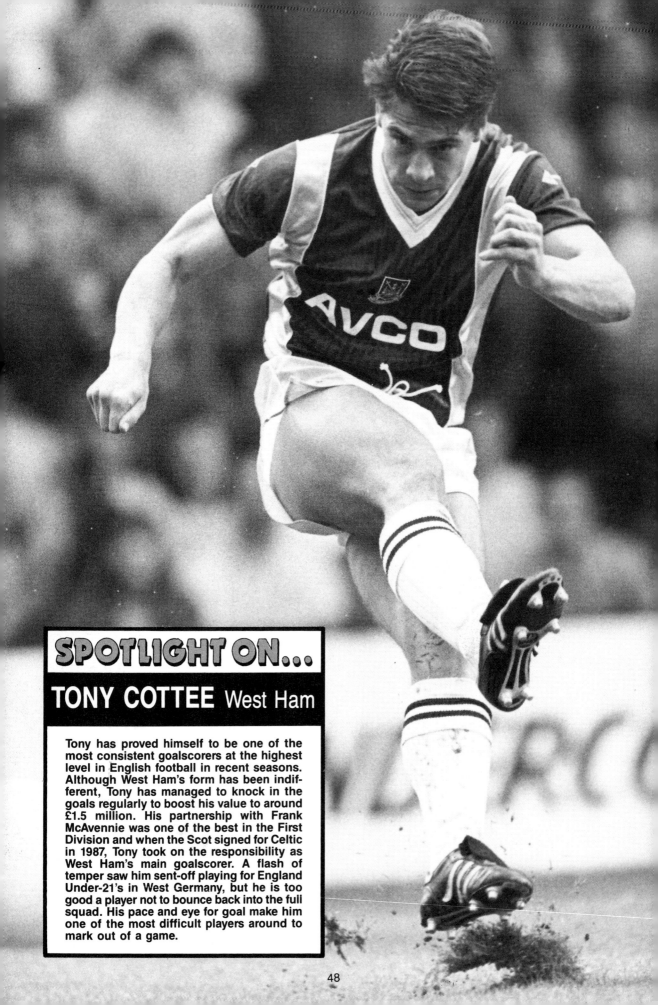

# SPOTLIGHT ON...

## TONY COTTEE West Ham

Tony has proved himself to be one of the most consistent goalscorers at the highest level in English football in recent seasons. Although West Ham's form has been indifferent, Tony has managed to knock in the goals regularly to boost his value to around £1.5 million. His partnership with Frank McAvennie was one of the best in the First Division and when the Scot signed for Celtic in 1987, Tony took on the responsibility as West Ham's main goalscorer. A flash of temper saw him sent-off playing for England Under-21's in West Germany, but he is too good a player not to bounce back into the full squad. His pace and eye for goal make him one of the most difficult players around to mark out of a game.

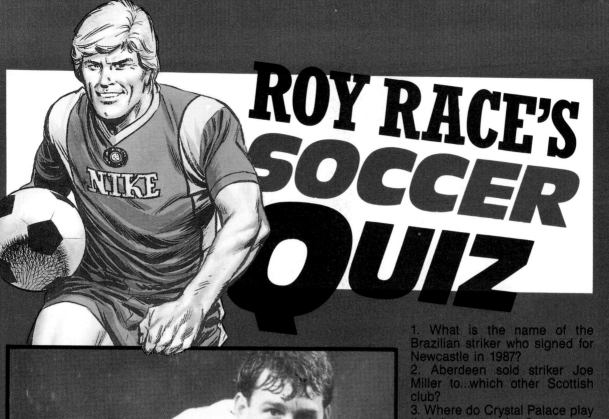

# ROY RACE'S SOCCER QUIZ

1. What is the name of the Brazilian striker who signed for Newcastle in 1987?

2. Aberdeen sold striker Joe Miller to...which other Scottish club?

3. Where do Crystal Palace play their home matches?

4. What was wrong with Spurs' shirts in the 1986/87 F.A. Cup Final against Coventry?

5. If David Rocastle was tackled by Des Walker, which two First Division clubs would be playing?

6. What is wrong with this statement: Brian Robson is the captain of England.

7. Who did Argentina beat in the Final of the 1986 World Cup?

8. Who was the manager of Southampton before Chris Nicholl?

9. Which country does David Phillips play for?

10. What is the nickname of Dave Bassett, who guided Wimbledon into the First Division before taking over at Watford...Henry, Harry or Hank?

11. In which colour shirts do Glasgow Rangers play?

**CONTINUED OVERLEAF** →

# ROY RACE'S SOCCER QUIZ

12. Which club is sometimes known as Pompey?

13. Alphabetically, which club is listed last in the Football League list (clue — they start with the letter 'Y').

14. Who are the sponsors of the Football League?

15. If you saw a game at Hillsborough, who would be the home club?

16. Plymouth in Devon or Cornwall?

17. Liverpool's Ray Houghton plays for the Republic of Ireland — but in which contry was he actually born?

18. Name the two Scottish clubs with the word 'Queen' in their name?

19. Which Spanish club did Howard Kendall join after leaving Everton as manager — Real Sociedad, Athletic Bilbao or Atletico Madrid?

20. Which club is known as the Sky Blues?

21. What is the full name of Brighton?

22. Is it Peterborough or Peterborough United?

23. Which Scottish club plays at Pittodrie?

24. Is Chelsea's Gordon Durie a defender, midfielder or striker?
25. Which Football league club plays in Cleethorpes?
26. Name the two big Edinburgh clubs.
27. From which club did Liverpool buy John Aldridge?
28. Who were the first Football League club to have articifial turf?
29. Which of the two Dundee clubs plays at Tannadice Park?
30. Who was the manager of Scotland during the 1986 World cup Finals in Mexico?
31. In which colours do Ian Rush's Juventus normally play?
32. Orient changed back to their original name a couple of seasons ago — what are they now called?
33. In which country do Sporting Lisbon play?

**CONTINUED OVERLEAF**

# ROY RACE'S SOCCER QUIZ

34. Where will the 1990 World Cup Finals be held?

35. Is it Paul Davis or Davies, the Arsenal midfield player?

36. In which stadium do Everton play their home games?

37. If the Tigers played the Lions, which clubs would be in action?

38. Which club has the initials P.N.E.?

39. Have Manchester City ever won the European Cup?

40. Who was manager of England before Bobby Robson?

41. What is the home ground of Southampton?

42. Name the great Northern Ireland goalkeeper who retired after the 1986 World Cup Finals.

43. With which club did Trevor Francis begin his career?

44. Brian Clough has won the Championship with Nottingham Forest and...which other club?

45. Who plays at Elland Road?

46. Malcolm Macdonald returned to management in 1987 with which club?

47. Name the Glasgow Rangers and England star who broke a leg in November, 1987.

48. Clive and Paul Allen play for Spurs, but who does Martin Allen play for?

49. Which West German club did Mark Hughes play for on loan last season?

50. Who won the World Cup in 1966?

## ROY'S ANSWERS

1. Mirandinha. 2. Celtic. 3. Selhurst Park. 4. They didn't all have the name of the club's sponsors on them. 5. Arsenal (Rocastle) and Nottingham Forest (Walker). 6. It's Bryan, not Brian Robson. 7. West Germany 3-2. 8. Lawrie McMenemy 9. Wales. 10. Harry. 11. Blue. 12. Portsmouth. 13. York City. 14. Barclays Bank. 15. Sheffield Wednesday. 16. Devon. 17. Scotland. 18. Queen of the South, Queens Park. 19. Athletic Bilbao. 20. Coventry City. 21. Brighton and Hove Albion. 22. Peterborough. 23. Aberdeen. 24. Striker. 25. Grimsby Town. 26. Hibernian and Hearts. 27. Oxford. 28. Queens Park Rangers. 29. Dundee United. 30. Alex Ferguson, now manager of Manchester United. 31. Black and white striped shirts. 32. Leyton Orient. 33. Portugal. 34. Italy. 35. Davis. 36. Goodison Park. 37. Hull v Millwall. 38. Preston North End. 39. No, but they did win the European Cup Winners Cup in 1970. 40. Ron Greenwood. 41. The Dell. 42. Pat Jennings. 43. Birmingham. 44. Derby. 45. Leeds. 46. Huddersfield. 47. Terry Butcher. 48. QPR. 49. Bayern Munich. 50. England.

RICK STEWART

# GOALKEEPER

IT WAS THE DYING SECONDS OF AN EXCITING YOUTH TEAM GAME BETWEEN OAKHAMPTON AND THEIR GREAT RIVALS BRANTPOOL...

IT'S *THERE*...!

A GREAT SHOT BY THE BRANTPOOL STRIKER! *UNSTOPPABLE*—!

*GOALKEEPER* RICK STEWART FLEW THROUGH THE AIR AT FULL STRETCH...

*NO!* HE—HE'S *SAVED* IT!

WHAT A *STOP!* THAT WAS *STUPENDOUS!*

THANKS TO RICK, THE SCORE'S STILL 0-0. HE'S KEPT US IN THE GAME.

*BUT* THERE WAS TO BE A LAST-MINUTE DRAMA...

AAAAH!

*FOUL, REF! PENALTY!*

HE'S *GIVEN* IT!

THE BALL WAS HIT HARD AND LOW... AND RICK WENT THE RIGHT WAY!

YEEESSSS! HE'S SAVED THAT ONE AS WELL!

BRILLIANT 'KEEPING! HE'S IN A CLASS OF HIS OWN!

IT'S ALL OVER! A GOALLESS DRAW!

RICK EARNED US THAT POINT ALMOST SINGLE-HANDED. WHAT A GOALIE!

AND THEN...

RICK... I'M LES NELSON, EDITOR OF THE OAKHAMPTON CLUB PROGRAMME. CAN I INTERVIEW YOU AFTER YOU'VE SHOWERED?

AN INTERVIEW? SURE, IF YOU WANT TO...

I WANT TO DO A PIECE ABOUT THE YOUTH TEAM, RICK. YOU'RE THE CAPTAIN, AND THE SIDE HAS HAD A GOOD SEASON...

BUT I'VE BEEN CHECKING BACK. DO YOU REALISE THAT, INCLUDING TODAY, YOU'VE ACTUALLY SAVED EIGHT PENALTIES THIS SEASON?

HAVE I? I DIDN'T REALISE.

HALF AN HOUR LATER...

THAT'S IT. THANKS, RICK. I THINK I'VE GOT ENOUGH NOW. YOU CAN SEE WHAT I WRITE IN THE PROGRAMME FOR THE CLUB'S LAST GAME.

MY PLEASURE, LES.

PROGRAMMES HAVE CHANGED A LOT SINCE I FIRST STARTED WATCHING FOOTBALL. I KNOW DAD USED TO KEEP ONE FROM EVERY MATCH *HE* PLAYED IN...

RICK'S FATHER, THE GREAT INTERNATIONAL GOALKEEPER, GORDON STEWART, HAD DIED TRAGICALLY IN AN AIR CRASH...

...AND RICK WAS TRYING DESPERATELY TO LIVE UP TO HIS IMAGE.

WELL, I NEVER KNEW *THAT* BEFORE!

WOW! THAT'S *FANTASTIC!*

OUR GORDON SETS NEW LEAGUE AND TYNEFIELD RECORD

**12** PENALTIES SAVED IN ONE SEASON!

IF I'VE SAVED EIGHT, I S'POSE I'M NOT DOING TOO BAD... BUT THERE'S NO WAY I CAN GET NEAR HIS RECORD THIS SEASON WITH ONLY THREE GAMES LEFT

BUT FOOTBALL CAN BE A STRANGE GAME, FULL OF COINCIDENCES...

OAKHAMPTON V. OSBORNE ATHLETIC

PENALTY!

HE HANDLED, REFEREE!

BUT...

ANOTHER INCREDIBLE SAVE BY RICK STEWART!

HE WAS ACROSS TO THAT ONE LIKE A FLASH!

THAT'S *ELEVEN* PENALTIES RICK'S SAVED NOW. I THINK THE LEAGUE RECORD IS TWELVE. I'M KEEPING MY PIECE FOR THE PROGRAMME ON ICE... JUST IN CASE!

LES NELSON WAS IN THE CROWD...

AND MORE EXCITEMENT WAS TO COME...

PENALTY!

AND ONCE MORE RICK PERFORMED THE IMPOSSIBLE!

WHAT'S THE OAKHAMPTON DEFENCE *PLAYING* AT?

I DON'T BELIEVE IT! THAT'S TWO FOR THE SECOND WEEK RUNNING!

SUPERB! HE'S UNBEATABLE, THIS 'KEEPER!

HOW DOES HE MANAGE TO STOP THEM?

RICK... I'VE LOOKED UP THE RECORD BOOKS. YOUR *DAD* HOLDS THE CURRENT PENALTY-SAVING RECORD, AND YOU'VE JUST EQUALLED IT! WHAT A STORY IF YOU SHOULD *BEAT* HIM!

FORGET IT, LES. THE CHANCES OF US CONCEDING ANOTHER PENALTY NEXT WEEK ARE NEXT TO IMPOSSIBLE!

# SPOTLIGHT ON...

## NEIL WEBB Nottingham Forest

Neil Webb went into the history books when he became the 1,000th player to be capped by England. The powerful Forest midfielder burst on to the international scene in 1987 and has been a permanent fixture in Bobby Robson's squad since. Neil was born in Reading and joined his home town club from school. He moved on to Portsmouth where he made more than 100 League appearances before signing for Forest for £250,000 in June, 1985. Neil will probably take over Bryan Robson's role in years to come for England.

Pat Bonner of Celtic and the Republic of Ireland.

# KEEP 'EM OUT!

England's Peter Shilton is probably worth 15 points a season to his club, Derby.

There's nothing like the thrill of seeing a goal scored...unless you're a goalkeeper. Here are some of the men who have to keep 'em out!

61

They say you have to be mad to be a goalkeeper...but the brave men who dive at forwards' flying feet are great entertainers, too.

Liverpool's extrovert Bruce Grobbelaar.

Norwich's Bryan Gunn makes a great save from John Aldridge of Liverpool.

Queens Park Rangers' David Seaman has established himself as England's number three 'keeper behind Peter Shilton and Chris Woods.

Luton's underrated Les Sealey makes a point.

Some people believe Neville Southall of Everton and Wales is now Britain's number one Number One.

Another huge kick from Wimbledon 'keeper and captain David Beasant.

Three of the best! Chris Woods, Peter Shilton and Gary Bailey, cruelly forced to retire after a knee injury.

# EUROPEAN ELITE

## GARY LINEKER
### BARCELONA

Gary started his career with Leicester before joining Everton for £800,000. One season and 30 goals later Gary signed for Barcelona in a £2 million deal after becoming the top scorer in the 1986 World Cup Finals with six goals as England reached the Quarter-Finals. Gary is on course to be England's leading goalscorer of all-time.

**RUUD GULLIT**
(AC MILAN AND HOLLAND)
Became the most expensive player in the world when he joined AC Milan from PSV Eindhoven for £5.5 million in 1986. The versatile star was an immediate hit in Italy and captained his country to the 1988 European Championship finals. Gullit was elected European Player of the Year in 1987.

## GLENN HYSEN
**(FIORENTINA & SWEDEN)**
The classy central defender was a target for Manchester United after helping Gothenburg beat Dundee United in the 1987 UEFA Cup Final. But the Swede opted for Italy and signed for Fiorentina, where his cool defensive play quickly made a big impression. Very dangerous at set pieces where he has scored a lot of goals.

**EUROPEAN ELITE**

### EMILIO BUTRAGUENO
**(REAL MADRID & SPAIN)**
Emilio is nicknamed the Vulture because of the way he swoops for goals.

The Real Madrid star is one of the most exciting and respected forwards in Europe and his goals have already helped the Spanish club to the Double.

A star of the 1986 World Cup Finals.

### IAN RUSH
**(JUVENTUS & WALES)**

Ian's goal-exploits with Liverpool made him an all-time great by the age of 25. His reward was a £3.2 million transfer to Juventus. His biggest regret is that he hasn't helped Wales qualify for the World Cup or European Championships, but time is on Ian's side and with his goalscoring record just about anything is possible.

## LIAM BRADY
### (WEST HAM & EIRE)

Sadly, the Republic of Ireland midfielder missed the first two 1988 European Championship Final ties through suspension. But in his career with Arsenal, Juventus, Sampdoria, Inter Milan, Ascoli and West Ham, "Chippy" has proved himself to be a star of the highest skill. Primarily a maker of goals, Liam has scored from some spectacular free-kicks.

### JOEL BATS
**(PARIS S-G & FRANCE)**

Joel grabbed the headlines in the 1986 World Cup as France's hero in the penalty shoot-out victory over Brazil, saving spot-kicks from Zico and Socrates. The Paris St. Germaine goalkeeper may be small for a keeper, but in Mexico he was a big hero as France finally lost in the Semi-Finals to West Germany.

# EUROPEAN ELITE

## OLEG BLOKHIN
### (DYNAMO KIEV & USSR)

The former European Footballer of the Year is recognised as one of the Soviet Union's greatest-ever players and his exciting wing play has been a feature of European football over the past 15 years. Fast, skilful and has a powerful shot.

## WILLEM KIEFT
(PSV & HOLLAND)

After a spell in Italian football with Pisa, Kieft returned to Holland to join PSV and helped them on an incredible unbeaten run in 1987/88. A dangerous striker, Kieft is strong on the ground and in the air while his unselfish running makes him the ideal team player.

**EUROPEAN ELITE**

## ALLY McCOIST
### (RANGERS & SCOTLAND)

Ally wasn't a success in England with Sunderland but the former St. Johnstone striker hardly stopped scoring for Glasgow Rangers last season. He'd notched up 27 goals by the first week in December which followed his role in helping Rangers to the title in 1986/87. Ally is a former Under-21 star now firmly established in the Scotland team.

**EUROPEAN ELITE**

### JOHN BARNES
(LIVERPOOL & ENGLAND)

John Barnes established himself as one of the most exciting players in the country with Watford. But since his £900,000 move to Liverpool in 1987, John has become a regular match-winner and crowd-pleaser, scoring some spectacular goals and creating many more. Perhaps still best known for his wonderful solo goal in Brazil in 1985.

**RUDI VOELLER**
(ROMA & W. GERMANY)
Began his career with Second Division 1860 Munich before joining Werder Bremen. Became top scorer in his first season in the Bundesliga and was named Footballer of the Year. A multi-million pound transfer took him to Roma after playing in the 1986 World Cup finals, where he impressed with his strength and skill.

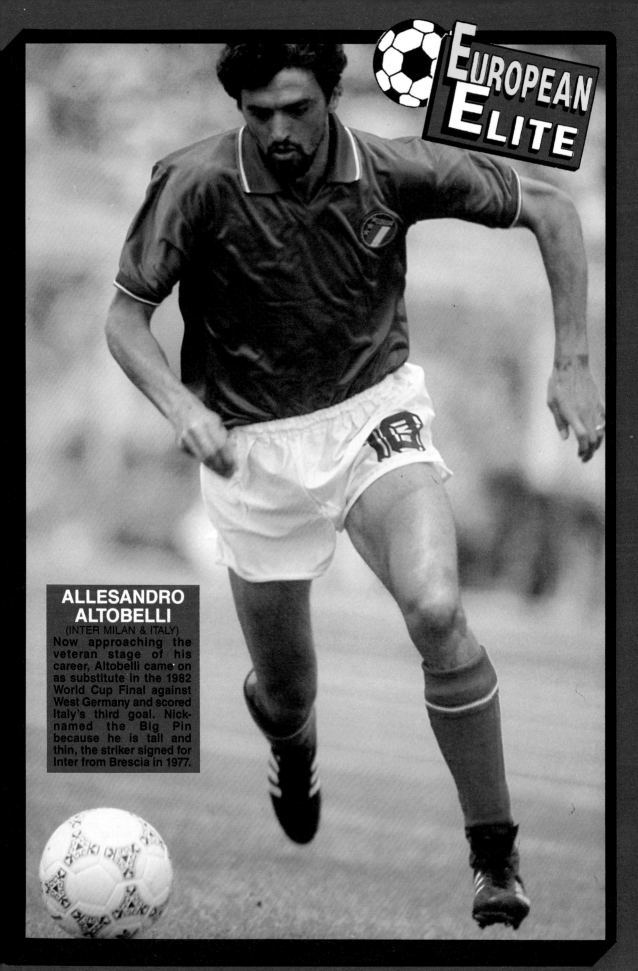

**ALLESANDRO ALTOBELLI**

(INTER MILAN & ITALY)
Now approaching the veteran stage of his career, Altobelli came on as substitute in the 1982 World Cup Final against West Germany and scored Italy's third goal. Nick-named the Big Pin because he is tall and thin, the striker signed for Inter from Brescia in 1977.

**MARK HUGHES**
(BARCELONA & WALES)
The former Manchester United striker found it difficult to settle in Barcelona following his £2 million transfer. In 1987, Mark was loaned to West German Champions Bayern Munich and started once again to show the form he displayed in the First Division. Mark has seen more ups and downs in five years than most players experience in their careers!

## MICHAEL LAUDRUP
### (JUVENTUS & DENMARK)
Michael was Ian Rush's partner at Juventus but three years previously the great Dane almost joined Rushie at Liverpool. That deal fell through and Michael went on to make a big name for himself in Italian football and in world football with Denmark.

**EUROPEAN ELITE**

## JOHNNY EKSTROM
### (EMPOLI & SWEDEN)

Came to the attention of England fans in September, 1986, when he scored a marvellous solo goal against Bobby Robson's team in a friendly. Ekstrom was linked with top English clubs but signed for Empoli and showed that he could score goals even in defensive minded Italy.

## SPOTLIGHT ON...
## MARK HATELEY England

Mark's dad, Tony, was known as "Have Boots Will Travel", because of the number of clubs he played for. Mark, too, has gained a lot of experience moving around after starting his career with Coventry. He moved on to Portsmouth where, before he had really established himself in English football, AC Milan paid a staggering £1 million to take him to Italy. His nickname there was Atilla because of his brave style of play and despite injuries, he made his mark with some fine goals. In 1986 Mark was the subject of another £1 million transfer when Monaco linked him and Glenn Hoddle in an attempt to win the French Championship. Although his England chances have been spasmodic, Mark is a valuable member of Bobby Robson's squad.

GOALA! GOALA! GOALA!

YEAHHHHH! GREAT! MAGIC! HE'S A MATCH-WINNER!

COULD BE! HE'S GOT LEGS LIKE MATCH-*STICKS*! HAW-HAW!

THE MON'S A *GREAT* FOOTBALLER! JUST THINK WHAT HE'D DO FOR PRINCES IF HE WAS IN *OUR* SIDE!

NOT A LOT!

OCH, HE'S A FREAK, MISTER McWHACKER!

*TWO DAYS LATER, AT THE PRINCES PARK GROUND...*

AREN'T YE PLAYING TODAY, DUNCAN?

NO. THE BOSS HAS BOUGHT SOME *NEW* BLOKE. STICKING HIM STRAIGHT IN. I'M SUB!

LADS... GIVE A GREAT BIG WELCOME TO YOUR NEW TEAM-MATE... *THE GREAT SPLOTZI!*

HIM!

I ALWAYS KNEW McWHACKER WAS BARMY!

YOU EVER PLAYED BEFORE, MATE?

I WAS IN MY *SCHOOL* TEAM!

YE'LL FIND PREMIER DIVISION FOOTBALL A BIT TOUGHER!

*THE GAME BEGAN...*

PRINCES! PRINCES! PRINCES!

OCH, THE POOR WEE MON LOOKS WORRIED! I'LL GI' HIM A WEE PASS TO GET HIM INTO THE GAME!

OOHHH! LOOK AT THAT! *NICE* BIT OF CONTROL FROM THE NEW MON!

HE'S DOING HIS *STAGE* ACT!

84

86

THEY ALL WENT TO THE FAIRGROUND...

I DON'T **LIKE** IT!

NOR DO I!

IT'S ONLY FOR **ONE** NIGHT! THE GREAT SPLOTZI HAS GONE HOME TO REST AFTER HIS EFFORTS FOR PRINCES! IT WAS PART OF THE DEAL!

LATER...

THE **TWO GREATEST** FOOTBALLERS ⭐ ON EARTH INSIDE!

ROLL UP! ROLL UP! FOR ONE NIGHT ONLY! THE **TWO** GREATEST FOOTBALLERS ON EARTH ... **NOW** SHOWING! SEE THEM PERFORM!

TICKETS

INSIDE...

BOOOOOOO! RUBBISH! WE WANT OUR MONEY BACK!

QUIET, PLEASE! NOW YOU WILL SEE HOT-SHOT HAMISH SHOWING YOU **HOW** TO **SCORE**!

GET OFF! YOU'RE USELESS!

OCH, AWA'! PLAYING PROPER FOOTBA'S EASIER THAN THIS ANYWAY!

AT THE END OF THE EVENING...

POOR OLD SPLOTZI WAS TOO TIRED TO PERFORM AFTER PLAYING PROPER FOOTBALL! BUT THE SHOW HAD TO GO ON!

DON'T SEE WHY **WE** HAD TO DO IT!

I WOULDN'T HAVE GOT BACK THE MONEY I PAID FOR SPLOTZI IF YE HADN'T TURNED OUT!

WHY COULDN'T YE DO IT YE'SELF?

OCH, I COULDNA' DO IT! I'M A **MANAGER**, NOT A PLAYER!

AYE, HE'S RIGHT THERE!

HE DOESN'T KNOW A PLAYER WHEN HE **SEES** ONE! HE OUGHT TO BE IN A CIRCUS!

The End

# ROY'S FAVOURITE STRIKERS

Hands up those who think Wimbledon's John Fashanu is one of the best strikers in the Football League! He's big, powerful and has more skill than he's given credit for ...a centre-forward who leads his line by example and with goals.

It hasn't been easy for Nigel Clough at Nottingham Forest having dad, Brian, as manager. But the England Under-21 striker is now accepted as a star in his own right.

Diego Maradona, the Argentina captain, comes away from his Napoli team-mate Salvatore Bagni of Italy in a friendly when Italy won 3-1.

Former Arsenal and Manchester United striker Frank Stapleton in his Ajax colours. The Republic of Ireland star battled to fitness after a back injury in 1986 that threatened his career.

One day Gary Lineker may well become England's top goalscorer of all-time...but here he is in action for Barcelona.

John Barnes of Liverpool (centre) is tackled by Arsenal's Michael Thomas, while £1.8 million Peter Beardsley looks on.

Whether it was for Glasgow Rangers or Scotland, Ally McCoist just couldn't stop scoring in a memorable 1987/88 season for the striker.

Former Chelsea favourite David Speedie, who joined Coventry for £800,000 in 1987. The Scot is a top class striker and competitor.

Kevin Sheedy (left) Everton's Republic of Ireland star, gets the better of this midfield tussle with West Ham's Mark Ward during a match at Upton Park.

90

# IRON BOY!

JEREMIAH JONES HAD THE REPUTATION OF BEING A WIMP... BUT IT WAS NOT ALTOGETHER HIS FAULT. HIS PARENTS WERE OLD-FASHIONED...

JEREMIAH... ARE YOU WEARING YOUR WOOLLY TODAY? THERE'S A CHILLY WIND...

WE DO WISH YOU WOULDN'T PLAY SILLY GAMES LIKE FOOTBALL!

I LOVE FOOTBALL. MUMS AND DADS NEVER SEEM TO UNDERSTAND. WE DON'T TALK THE SAME LANGUAGE.

JEREMIAH AND CHRISTOPHER SMITH HAD ALWAYS BEEN FRIENDS...

HUH! IF YOU ASK ME, WE'RE JUST LIKE SMITH AND JONES ON TELLY! A BIT OF A JOKE. LET'S HOPE WE CAN DO THE BUSINESS AGAINST BARNS HILL TODAY.

HIYA, JEREMIAH. HOW'S IT GOING?

NOT BAD, I SUPPOSE, CHRIS. USUAL PARENT PROBLEMS. THEY THINK FOOTBALL'S THE SAME GAME FOR US THAT THEY SEE ON TELLY. ALL HOOLIGANISM.

WE WILL, MATE...WE WILL.

THE TWO PLAYED FOR FANTHORPE ALBION...

IT'S ALL HE WORRIES ABOUT... APPEARANCES!

THAT'S WHY WE GET HAMMERED EVERY WEEK!

COME ALONG, COME ALONG, BOYS. I LIKE YOU HERE EARLY SO WE CAN GET YOU LOOKING NICE BEFORE YOU GO OUT.

JEREMIAH PLAYED AT LEFT-BACK...

LOOK AT THAT LITTLE GUY. A PUFF OF WIND WOULD BLOW HIM OVER.

LET'S PLAY ON HIM THEN.

OH, NICE BALL PLAY, JEREMIAH!

JEREMIAH? WHAT A NAME!

TAKE HIM OUT!

MAKE HIS TEETH RATTLE!

UUUGGGHHH!

AND NO MATTER HOW HARD JEREMIAH TRIED...

LOVELY STUFF, BARNS HILL! WE'RE BEATING THEM EASILY!

AAAHHH!

I'M ACHING ALL OVER, CHRIS— AND THERE'S STILL THE SECOND HALF TO COME. WHY IS IT I'M SO SMALL... AND EVERYONE ELSE IS SO BIG?

IT'S NOT YOUR FAULT, JEREMIAH... YOU'RE GOOD AT FOOTBALL!

WALKING THROUGH THE PARK WAS A BLUE-EYED, SQUARE-JAWED MAN...

THAT LOOKS LIKE YOUNG JEREMIAH JONES FROM UP THE STREET.

OWCHH! THEY'RE GIVING THE POOR WEE BOY A REAL CLATTERING. AND HE'S A GOOD PLAYER, TOO...

LOOK, CHRIS, OVER THERE! IT'S MISTER McTAVISH FROM DOWN THE STREET.

HE'S A REAL TOUGH NUT. THEY SAY HE WAS IN THE S.A.S.

CAN I HAVE A WORD, LADDIE... IN PRIVATE!

ER... SURE, MISTER McTAVISH.

SEE YOU LATER, CHRIS.

YOU'VE GOT SKILL, BOY...YOU'VE GOT TALENT. BUT YOU LET YOURSELF GET KNOCKED ABOUT. REMEMBER... A GOOD LITTLE 'UN LIKE YOU, WILL ALWAYS BEAT A GOOD BIG 'UN!

BUT YOU'VE GOT TO BE TOUGH, LADDIE... BOTH IN MIND AND BODY! THAT'S THE SECRET. AND I'D LIKE TO HELP YOU...

S.A.S. THE SPECIAL AIR SERVICE. A HERO. THAT'S WHAT EVERY-ONE SAYS. AND HE'S INTERESTED IN ME—!

YES, PLEASE, MISTER McTAVISH. WE'RE PLAYING BATTLETOWN ON SATURDAY IN THE CUP— AND THEY'RE A BUNCH OF BRUISERS!

JUST ONE WEEK, EH? THEN WE'VE GOT TIME TO MAKE A BIT OF DIFFERENCE... AS LONG AS YOU WORK FOR EVERY AVAILABLE MINUTE. REPORT TO ME AT 0600 HOURS IN THE MORNING.

ER— ALL RIGHT, MISTER McTAVISH!

AND SO...

STOP YAWNING, LAD. YOU'LL BE TIRED LATER.. NOT NOW!

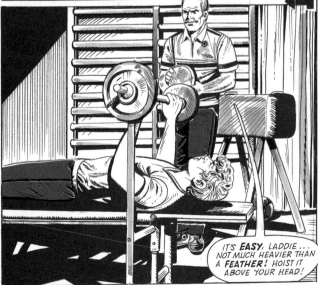

BUT AT LAST...

NOT BAD... NOT BAD AT ALL. YOU'RE NOT **QUITE** THE IRON BOY, BUT YOU'RE IN BETTER SHAPE TO FACE BATTLE-TOWN TOMORROW!

AND SO...

LOOK AT THAT LITTLE KID, FRED. HE'S TINY.

HE'LL BE MARKING YOU... SEE HOW LONG IT TAKES TO STAMP HIM IN THE GROUND!

OH, CRUMBS!

JEREMIAH! **WHAT** DID I TELL YOU?

OH! ER... **BE TOUGH IN MIND AND BODY**, MISTER McTAVISH!

AND IN THE VERY FIRST ATTACK...

A **FEROCIOUS** TACKLE!

THE LITTLE LAD'S KNOCKED HIM FOR SIX AND COME AWAY WITH THE BALL!

OWWCCHH!

CONFIDENCE FLOWED THROUGH JEREMIAH...

I FEEL TEN FEET TALL! I MAY ONLY BE SMALL, BUT I FEEL AS GOOD AS KENNY SANSOM!

## SPOTLIGHT ON...
### JOHN FASHANU
### Wimbledon

John's first League club was Cambridge but he made his League debut with Norwich, who released him on a free transfer after a loan spell with Crystal Palace. John moved on to Lincoln where his goals prompted George Graham to pay £55,000 to bring him to Millwall. He became Wimbledon's record signing at £120,00 in 1986 and after making his mark in Division One, John whose brother Justin once played for Nottingham Forest, was rated in the £1 million bracket.

When Graeme Souness became player-manager of Glasgow Rangers in 1986, he decided that the best way to achieve success in Scotland was to... buy English stars! And these are just some of the players who have helped the Scottish Explosion...

Trevor Francis, a former Sampdoria team-mate of Souness's, in action against Dynamo Kiev.

THE

Dundee United's goal heroes in Barcelona...Iain Ferguson and John Clark, after their 2-1 win in the Nou Camp stadium.

Dundee United's David Narey is on the ball against Barcelona's Gary Lineker in the 1986/87 UEFA Cup Quarter Final which the Scottish club won 3—1 on aggregate.

# SCOTTISH EXPLOSION

They're MacTerrific! Terry Butcher, Chris Woods and Graham Roberts celebrate Rangers' title success in 1986/7.

Rangers' captain Terry Butcher is comforted by his wife Rita after breaking a leg against Aberdeen in November, 1987.

Mark Falco who left Rangers for Queens Park Rangers for £350,00.

Rangers' goal machine Ally McCoist holds off Sergei Baltacha of Dynamo Kiev.

100

Souness led Rangers to the Scottish Premier Division in his first season in charge and his spending power meant that many top internationals were tempted North of the Border to Scotland.

After winning just about everything with Liverpool, Graeme Souness is heading towards similar success with Rangers.

# JIMMY of CITY

CLIVE CHELSEY HAD JUST BEEN TELLING SOME OF HIS FRIENDS HOW JIMMY HAD ONCE STOPPED JACK FROM GIVING UP FOOTBALL, IN THEIR EARLY DAYS AS PLAYERS. HIS SISTER PAT HAD REMINDED HIM THAT THERE HAD BEEN AN OCCASION WHEN JACK HAD DONE A SIMILAR SERVICE FOR JIMMY. THE PARTY REACHED A COFFEE BAR, AND WERE EAGER TO HEAR THE DETAILS...

COME ON, PAT, YOU CAN'T JUST LEAVE US WONDERING. LET'S HEAR THE FULL STORY.

I DON'T NEED TO TELL YOU THAT JACK AND JIMMY HAVE ALWAYS BEEN ALMOST EXACT OPPOSITES IN EVERY WAY. THAT'S WHAT MAKES THEM SUCH A POWERFUL COMBINATION NOW THAT THEY'RE BOTH PLAYING FOR CASTLEBURN CITY.

"JACK HAS ALWAYS BEEN CAREFUL WITH MONEY, AND JIMMY WILDLY EXTRAVAGANT. THIS ALL HAPPENED IN THEIR FIRST SEASON, WHEN JACK WAS WITH UNITED. JIMMY CAME IN ONE DAY WEARING A FABULOUS NEW OUTFIT."

GOOD GRIEF!

WHAT DO YOU THINK OF IT, THEN?

YOU HAVEN'T DARED TO WALK THROUGH THE STREETS IN *THAT*, SURELY?

I THINK IT'S *FAB*!

IT MUST HAVE BEEN TERRIBLY EXPENSIVE.

IT WAS.

YOU GAVE *MONEY* FOR IT? THE TAILOR SHOULD HAVE PAID *YOU* TO TAKE IT OUT OF THE SHOP!

AT THAT MOMENT THE BACK DOOR-BELL RANG.

WHOEVER CAN THAT BE? I'D BETTER SEE.

WE'RE DELIVERING YOUR NEW DEEP FREEZE, MRS CHELSEY.

THERE MUST BE SOME MISTAKE. IT'S LOVELY. BUT *I* DIDN'T ORDER IT. IT'S NOT MINE.

YES, IT *IS* YOURS, MUM. A LITTLE PRESSY FROM JACK AND ME. WE WENT HALVES ON IT.

IT'S MARVELLOUS OF YOU BOTH. I'VE BEEN LONGING FOR ONE OF THESE FOR AGES.

BUT WHEN JACK GOT JIMMY ALONE...

I THOUGHT WE AGREED TO BUY IT *NEXT MONTH*, JIM? WE HAVEN'T SAVED UP ENOUGH YET.

YOU KNOW ME... I HATE WAITING. IT'S ALL RIGHT, THOUGH. I ONLY HAD TO PAY A DEPOSIT. WE'VE GOT FOUR WEEKS TO FIND THE REST.

THE FOLLOWING DAY, CITY WERE AT HOME TO IRONCASTLE. JIMMY HAD ALREADY BOUGHT HIMSELF AN EXPENSIVE CAR, BUT JACK WAS QUITE CONTENT TO TRAVEL TO UNITED'S STADIUM BY BUS.

I'LL NEED TO BUY SOME PETROL, AND I'M SKINT. CAN YOU LEND ME A COUPLE OF QUID, JACK?

IT'S A GOOD JOB ONE OF US TAKES CARE OF HIS MONEY.

I DON'T UNDERSTAND IT. I EARN AS MUCH AS YOU — YET I NEVER HAVE ENOUGH.

YOU NEVER WILL HAVE ENOUGH IF YOU DON'T LEARN TO LOOK AFTER IT. YOU CHUCK POUND NOTES ABOUT LIKE CONFETTI.

THE OPENING OF CITY'S GAME AGAINST IRONCASTLE WENT WELL FOR JIMMY!

IT'S THERE!

CITY ARE ONE UP ALREADY!

GREAT SHOT, JIMMY!

WHEN THE IRONCASTLE DEFENDERS RECOVERED FROM THE EARLY SHOCK, THEY MARKED JIMMY TIGHTLY AND GAVE HIM LITTLE ROOM TO MOVE UNTIL SHORTLY BEFORE HALF-TIME...

THEY'VE LET JIMMY OFF THE HOOK. HE'S FREE!

GOOD THINKING BY JIMMY—BUT HE'S GETTING NO SUPPORT.

HE'S IN POSSESSION, BUT THERE'S NOTHING POSITIVE HE CAN DO WITH THE BALL.

TO THE AMAZEMENT OF THE FANS JIMMY FOUND A WAY THROUGH THE DEFENDERS WITH A BRILLIANTLY ANGLED SHOT!

GOOOAAL!

2-0 TO CITY!

NO-ONE BUT JIMMY COULD HAVE FOUND THE WAY TO STICK THAT IN!

AT HALF-TIME CITY SKIPPER TREVOR SCOTT WAS FULL OF PRAISE FOR JIMMY'S PERFORMANCE.

A COUPLE OF NICE GOALS, JIMMY.

I'M LOOKING FORWARD TO MAKING IT A HAT-TRICK IN THE SECOND-HALF!

MANAGER IAN CLARK DISAPPROVED OF JIMMY'S REMARK, AND CALLED HIM BACK AS THE PLAYERS RAN OUT.

SCORING A HAT-TRICK ISN'T *THAT* IMPORTANT, JIMMY. YOU'RE NOT JUST PLAYING FOR YOURSELF. REMEMBER YOU'RE ONE OF A *TEAM!*

JIMMY THREW HIMSELF ENERGETICALLY INTO THE SECOND HALF.

JIMMY'S AWAY AGAIN. THIS COULD BE HIS THIRD...!

MANAGER IAN CLARK WINCED AS A DEFENDER PILED INTO JIMMY.

OOOUCH! THAT COULD HAVE DONE JIMMY SOME DAMAGE. I THINK IT WOULD BE WISE TO HAVE HIM OFF.

IAN WANTS YOU OFF, JIMMY.

OH, NO! WHY SHOULD HE? I'M ALL RIGHT.

JIMMY WAS RESENTFUL AT BEING CALLED BACK TO THE BENCH, ESPECIALLY WHEN, JUST BEFORE THE END, THE SUBSTITUTE HEADED A *THIRD* GOAL!

THAT COULD HAVE BEEN MY HAT-TRICK—IF IAN CLARK HAD GIVEN ME THE CHANCE!

JIMMY WAS STILL FEELING LET DOWN WHEN HE GOT INTO HIS CAR TO DRIVE HOME, AND A COMPLETE STRANGER APPEARED...

YOUR PARDON, SIGNOR CHELSEY. MAY I HAVE YOUR PERMISSION TO SPEAK? IT COULD BE TO YOUR GREAT ADVANTAGE.

THE CHELSEY FAMILY WERE AMAZED WHEN JIMMY BROUGHT THE STRANGER HOME.

THIS IS SIGNOR BOLONI, FROM ITALY. SIGNOR— MY MOTHER.

CHARMING LADY. I KEESE YOUR 'AND.

YUK!

SIGNOR BOLONI IS A TALENT SCOUT FOR THE RICHEST CLUB IN ITALY. HE'S OFFERED ME FABULOUS TERMS TO SIGN FOR THEM.

BUT YOU WOULDN'T LEAVE CITY...!

HE CAN'T! HE'S GOT A CONTRACT!

MY CLUB WILL NEGOTIATE WITH CITY. THEESE IS A GREAT CHANCE FOR JIMMY. WE WILL MAKE HIM REECH AND WORLD FAMOUS!

WHEN BOLONI HAD GONE, THE FAMILY TRIED TO ARGUE WITH JIMMY, BUT HE WAS TOO DAZZLED BY THE ITALIAN OFFER TO LISTEN.

IT'S NO USE TRYING TO TALK ME OUT OF IT. THIS IS THE CHANCE OF A LIFETIME. THEY'RE OFFERING ME A SUPER FIVE-YEAR CONTRACT. I COULD END UP ALMOST A MILLIONAIRE.

THE FAMILY SAW VERY LITTLE OF JIMMY DURING THE NEXT FEW DAYS.

IT'S NO USE WAITING FOR JIMMY. HE SPENDS ALL HIS TIME WITH SIGNOR BOLONI.

LIVING IT UP, FROM WHAT I HEAR. BOLONI HAS THE BEST SUITE IN THE MOST EXPENSIVE HOTEL. HE MUST BE RUNNING UP A TERRIFIC BILL.

CITY MANAGER IAN CLARK ARRIVED UNEXPECTEDLY, WITH THE TEAM CAPTAIN, TREVOR SCOTT.

JACK, CAN'T YOU TALK JIMMY OUT OF THIS MAD IDEA? IF HE PERSISTS HE'LL CAUSE SCANDALOUS TROUBLE FOR HIMSELF AND THE CLUB.

MAYBE I'LL HAVE A TRY. BUT HE SEEMS COMPLETELY BESOTTED BY THIS MAN BOLONI.

WHEN JIMMY CAME HOME, JACK TRIED IN VAIN TO TALK SOME SENSE INTO HIM.

I'VE LEARNT THAT YOU'VE GOT TO GRAB CHANCES AND LOOK AFTER YOURSELF IN THIS GAME. NO-ONE ELSE WILL. WHAT HAPPENED AGAINST IRONCASTLE SHOWED ME THAT CITY WOULD DROP ME LIKE A HOT BRICK IF IT SUITED THEM.

THE FOLLOWING MORNING...

GOODNESS, THE CLOCK'S STOPPED. WHAT'S THE RIGHT TIME, JIMMY?

SORRY. I DON'T KNOW.

WHY NOT? WHAT HAPPENED TO THAT SUPER WRIST WATCH YOU SPENT A FORTUNE ON THE OTHER WEEK?

I'VE LENT IT TO SIGNOR BOLONI. HE FORGOT TO BRING ONE FROM ITALY.

AS THE WEEK WENT BY, JACK GREW INCREASINGLY WORRIED BY JIMMY'S IMPETUOUS BEHAVIOUR.

I'LL WALK WITH YOU TO THE BUS STOP.

WHY? WHAT'S HAPPENED TO YOUR CAR?

I'VE SOLD IT. I'LL BUY A BETTER ONE IN ITALY. I'VE GIVEN THE MONEY TO BOLONI, FOR OUR AIR FARES. CURRENCY REGULATIONS HAVE HELD UP CHANGING HIS ITALIAN MONEY INTO ENGLISH. MY NEW CLUB WILL PAY IT ALL BACK WHEN WE REACH ITALY.

I THINK YOU'RE RAVING MAD.

NOTHING THAT JIMMY'S FAMILY OR FRIENDS SAID TO HIM COULD CHANGE HIS MIND...

JIMMY'S PACKED, AND NOW HE'S GONE TO THE HOTEL TO MAKE FINAL ARRANGEMENTS WITH THAT DREADFUL ITALIAN. THEY'RE FLYING TO ROME SOME TIME TONIGHT.

I'M GOING TO PHONE TREVOR SCOTT AND ASK HIM TO COME ROUND HERE WITH ONE OR TWO PALS.

TREVOR SCOTT ARRIVED WITH CITY PLAYERS PADDY MURPHY AND DUSTY MILLER.

SINCE JIMMY WON'T LISTEN TO REASON WE'LL HAVE TO TAKE DRASTIC MEASURES. IF NOTHING ELSE WILL STOP HIM LEAVING, WE'LL HAVE TO PREVENT HIM BY FORCE!

YOU MEAN — LIKE — KIDNAP HIM?

SORT OF. WE'LL GRAB HIM AND LOCK HIM IN HIS ROOM AND I'LL STAND GUARD OVER HIM UNTIL IT'S TOO LATE TO CATCH THE PLANE.

HE'LL KICK UP A LOT OF NOISE. DISTURB THE FAMILY AND THE WHOLE NEIGHBOUR-HOOD.

ISN'T THERE ANYWHERE ELSE WE COULD DUMP HIM FOR A FEW HOURS?

YES. THAT GIVES ME A BETTER IDEA. THERE'S A STRONG SHED RIGHT AT THE BOTTOM OF THE GARDEN. WHILE I'M PUTTING A BED AND ONE OR TWO THINGS IN IT, YOU GO AND COLLAR HIM AS HE LEAVES THE HOTEL. YOU CAN TAKE HIM STRAIGHT THERE WITHOUT COMING TO THE HOUSE AT ALL.

THE THREE CITY PLAYERS DROVE TO THE HOTEL AND WAITED.

THERE HE IS!

FOLLOW HIM, TREV, UNTIL HE GETS TO WHERE THE STREET LIGHTING ISN'T SO BRIGHT. THEN WE'LL POUNCE.

RIGHT. GET THAT SACK AND THE PIECE OF ROPE READY.

AND, MINUTES LATER...

ARRRGH!

GAAH!

RIGHT. INTO THE CAR WITH HIM!

JACK WAS WAITING...

WELL DONE. DUMP HIM ON THE BED, AND I'LL LOCK HIM IN!

WITH THE VICTIM SAFE INSIDE, JACK PADLOCKED THE DOOR.

YOU'RE IN FOR A FEW UNCOMFORTABLE HOURS, JIMMY BOY. BUT IT'S FOR YOUR OWN GOOD.

HE'LL BE HOPPING MAD WHEN WE LET HIM OUT.

BUT HE'LL BE GRATEFUL TO US ONE DAY.

COME ON UP TO THE HOUSE. MUM USUALLY MAKES COFFEE ABOUT THIS TIME.

THANKS, WE WILL!

SOUNDS GREAT!

A CUP OF COFFEE WOULD GO DOWN WELL JUST NOW.

NOT A WORD ABOUT YOU-KNOW-WHO LOCKED IN THE SHED. I DON'T THINK MUM WOULD APPROVE.

BUT THE CONSPIRATORS WERE IN FOR A SHOCK!

JIMMY! HOW DID YOU GET OUT?

OUT OF WHERE? I'VE BEEN HANGING ABOUT AT THE AIRPORT, HOPING THAT DIRTY CROOK BOLONI WOULD TURN UP. THERE WAS NO FLIGHT BOOKED. HE DIDN'T USE ANY OF THE MONEY I GAVE HIM TO BUY TICKETS OR PAY HIS HOTEL BILLS. HE'S SWINDLED ME OUT OF THE LOT.